TOP THAT! * ACTIVITY * FUN * LEARNING

On the Seashore

A Copy Coloring Book.

Published by Top That! Publishing plc
Tide Mill Way, Woodbridge, Suffolk, IP12 1AP, UK
www.topthatpublishing.com
Copyright © 2012 Top That! Publishing plc
0 2 4 6 8 9 7 5 3 1
Printed and bound in China

Jellyfish

Jellyfish live everywhere in the sea and come in all shapes and sizes, from very tiny jellyfish to big jellyfish with enormous tentacles. Most jellyfish are harmless, but be careful of swimming near to them because their tentacles may sting if you get too close.

Shore Crab

The shore crab is the most common kind of crab. Shore crabs are always getting into fights with each other, and if you ever see one in the wild it will often be missing claws or legs. Luckily for the crabs, they grow back.

Starfish

Starfish have no front or back and can move in any direction without turning. They have an eye on each arm but cannot see color, only light and dark. Most starfish have five arms, and they have hundreds of tiny feet all over their bodies to move them across the rocks and coral.

Seagull

Seagulls are large, noisy birds found all over the world, especially by the sea. Seagulls will eat anything they find, but the biggest and bravest gulls have been known to snatch food out of peoples' hands!

Sea Anemones

Sea anemones look like beautiful underwater flowers, but they are actually predators, eating fish and crustaceans. Sea anemones come in all kinds of amazing shapes, sizes and colors. Little creatures are attracted into their tentacles, where they are stung and then digested.

Mantis Shrimp

The mantis shrimp is a fierce predator that likes to eat other shrimp, crabs and fish. It can grow up to 12 in. long and will use its club-like claws to pummel prey to death. The mantis shrimp's eyes are capable of moving 360° to see all around.

Seahorse

Seahorses are one of the most magical and graceful animals in the sea. Their peculiar appearance and beautiful, changing colors have amazed people for hundreds of years. Seahorses have unusual breeding behavior. The female lays eggs in the male seahorse's pouch and he carries the baby seahorses until they hatch.

Godwit

The godwit is a very rare and beautiful seashore bird. They have long, slightly upturned bills, which allows them to dig deep in the sand for worms. Godwits migrate south towards warmer weather in the winter.

Seal

There are many different kinds of seal and they are very common around harbors and rocky coastlines all across the world. Seals are excellent swimmers and can travel very fast underwater, but they spend most of their time out of the water playing, grooming and sleeping.

Moray Eel

The longest species of moray eel can reach up to 13 ft in length, and is found in the Pacific Ocean. Moray eels have long, muscular bodies and blunt teeth for crushing prey. They usually hide in rock or coral crevices, darting out to catch their prey.

Rockhopper Penguin

Rockhopper penguins are part of the crested penguin family due to the brightly-colored feathers on their heads. Unlike other penguins who slide on their bellies, or climb to avoid obstacles, rockhopper penguins will jump over boulders or cracks in rocks.

Dogfish

Dogfish are actually small sharks. They have large, sharp teeth for eating everything in sight, but they are not dangerous to humans. Dogfish lay their eggs in tiny pockets called "mermaid's purses", which the young fish hatch out of when they are ready.

Sea Otter

Sea otters are very playful, friendly animals. Found in the coastal areas of the northen and eastern North Pacific Ocean, they have a thick coat of fur to help keep them warm. Sea otters have learned to use tools like a human. They will use rocks to smash open shells for the food inside, and to dig up prey.

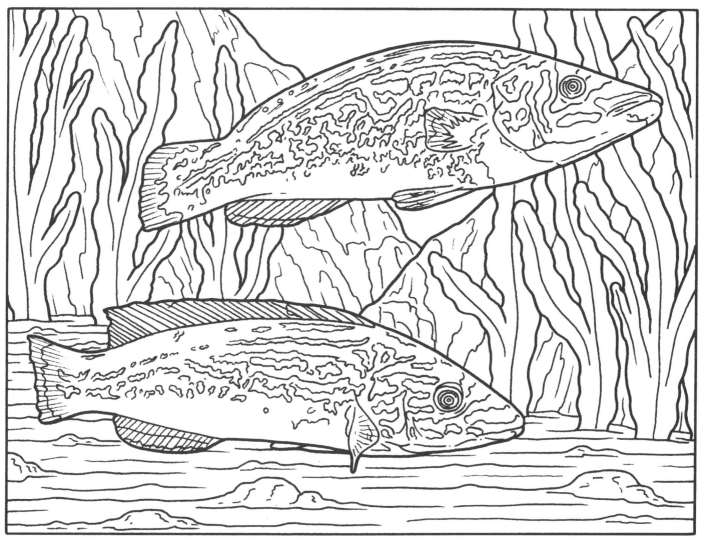

Cuckoo Wrasse

The cuckoo wrasse is a brightly colored, curious fish that will often swim up to divers. However, although they look beautiful, they have spiny fins and hundreds of teeth in their mouth and all the way down their throat for gobbling up food.

Shells

When some seashore animals die, their shells wash up empty with the tide. Hundreds of shells can be found just by walking along the shore, and they can teach us the secrets of the amazing animals that once lived inside. Over time these shells will crumble into the sand of the seashore and become home to millions of other animals.

Avocet

The avocet's bright white feathers and jet black markings make them one of the most striking birds on our seashores. They have long, upturned beaks to scoop up insects and worms from the floor of shallow coastal marshes and lagoons.

Dolphin

Dolphins can be spotted all over the world—from colder northern and southern waters to warm tropical waters. They are very clever and friendly animals, who love human attention and playing games. Dolphins make high pitched squeaking and clicking noises to communicate with each other and live in groups called pods, of up to twelve dolphins.

Long-spined Sea Scorpion

Long-spined sea scorpions have a large head with huge eyes and mouth to ambush their prey. Found on rocky ground, they vary in color depending upon their particular surroundings. Their distinctive feature is the very long spine found on their cheeks.

Mudskipper

Mudskippers are very unusual fish. They are the only fish in the world that can actually survive out of water, and are often found perching on rocks or resting on sandbars when the tide goes out. Mudskippers hunt around mangrove swamps looking for insects, sandworms and small crustaceans to eat.

Hermit Crab

Unlike other crabs, hermit crabs do not have a permanent hard shell for protection. Their bodies are very soft so they live in other animals' empty shells. Hermit crabs have to carry these shells all the time and will only creep out when they have found another shell to live in.

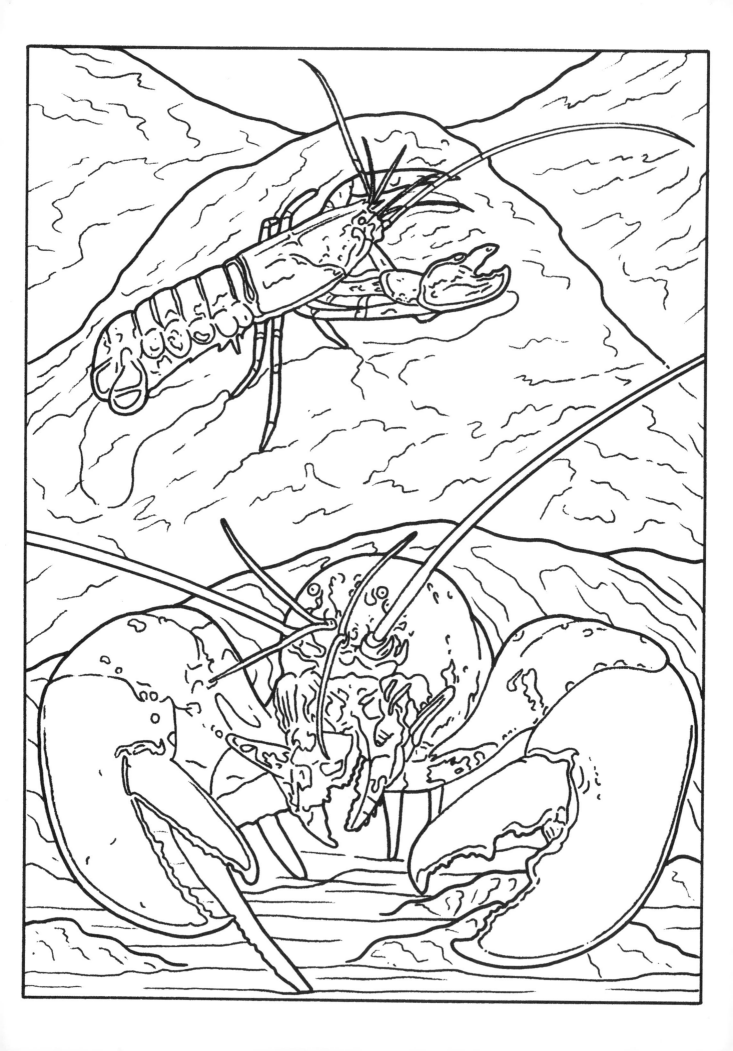

Lobster

Lobsters are found in all oceans, living on rocky or muddy seabeds. Many people think that lobsters are bright red, but they only actually turn red when they are cooked! In the wild they are a dark green-blue color. Lobsters usually hunt for food, which includes fish and crabs, at night.

Fiddler Crab

Male fiddler crabs have one normal claw and one massive claw! If the crab loses its large claw, a new one will grow on the opposite side after the crab has shed and regrown its shell.

Baby Turtle

Although adult turtles live in the ocean, they have to travel to the shore to lay their eggs. When the baby turtles hatch they race to the sea where they will be safe from predators such as gulls and crabs. In the wild, sea turtles can live to be eighty years old.